The stories at this level

The stories at this level are more varied in the
complex plots. The West Street characters, h
centre of the stories, and thus give children a
familiarity.

There are more legends and traditional stories at this level, some of which
are in verse, as it is important that children should relish and enjoy the
rhythms and sound patterns of rhymes, even if they do not understand
every word.

The stories begin to go beyond children's everyday experiences by
introducing fantasy and life in the past. This will help to extend your child's
horizons; you may want to make direct comparisons between your child's
experiences and what happens to the other people in the stories.

Before you start reading with your child, read the story and activities first
yourself, so that you become familiar with the text and the best way to give
it expression and emphasis when reading it aloud.

Always sit comfortably with your child, so that both of you can see the
book easily.

Read the story to your child, making it sound as interesting as possible.
Encourage your child to participate actively in the reading, to turn over the
pages and to become involved in the story and characters.

If your child seems confident, you may miss out your own first reading.
Suggest that you read the story together the first time. Carry your child's
reading along with your own, without slowing up or losing fluency or
expression. Do this again, but tell your child that you will stop reading
when you get a signal (for example a push on the arm), and will start
reading again when given another signal. Then say "Do you want to read
the story all on your own now?"

Finish by asking if you should read the whole story again to your child.
Then say "Now you might like to go away and read the story to yourself
(or to Teddy or a younger brother or sister) when you feel like it."

The activities at this level

The activities need not be completed at once. They are not a test, but will help your child to remember the words and stories and to develop further the skills required for becoming a fluent reader.

The activities are often divided into three parts.

One part is designed to encourage discussion about the stories, and to link them where possible with the child's own experiences. Encourage your child to predict what will happen and to recall the main events of the story. Change the wording of the story as much as you like and encourage your children to tell you about the story in their own way.

One part encourages children to look back through the book to find general or specific things in the text or the pictures. The child learns to begin to look at the text itself, and to recognise individual words and letters more precisely. The activities state clearly when you should give a letter its name, and when you should sound it out. The activities also introduce more writing, largely copying from words in the original story. If your children find this too difficult, copy the words onto a piece of paper for them to trace over.

One part is headed *Things to do* and consists of activities which your child can do without your help. You may have to read the instructions for the activities first. Suggest that your child tries reading them with you, and then reads them back to you without your help. It is not necessary to repeat the original words exactly, but your child should understand what the instructions mean. Then leave your child to carry out the first activity alone.

If your child wishes to go on to the next activity immediately, this is fine, but don't insist on it. You may find that the instructions have been read and the activity carried out without you knowing it! This is excellent. Always discuss what your child has done, and give plenty of praise and encouragement.

Your child might like to build up a 'Book of things I have done from my stories'. This would give a sense of achievement and permanence, as well as enabling you to keep a check on development and what has been done.

When all the activities have been done, encourage your child to read the story again before you move on to another book. Your child should now feel secure with it and enjoy reading to you.

Tamla's cat

by Helen Arnold

Illustrated by Tony Kenyon

A Piccolo Original
In association with Macmillan Education

Tamla had a cat.
She was a get-in-the-way,
tickle-your-nose,
snuffle-your-ear,
lie-on-your-bed,
play-with-your-wool
cat called Moo.

She was called Moo because
she liked milk.
And because she made a noise which
was more like a moo than a mew.

When she was awake she purred,
or she hissed at the dog next door,
or she said nothing.

One cold morning Moo wasn't there.
She wasn't on Tamla's bed.
She wasn't drinking her milk.
She wasn't hissing at the dog.
She wasn't anywhere.

Then Mum found that
her ball of wool had gone.
"Where's my wool?" she said.

Dad found that his scarf had gone.
"Where's my scarf?" he said.

Tamla found that her socks had gone.
"Where are my socks?" she said.
"And where is Moo?"

"Moo, Moo, where are you?"
called Tamla.
Tamla looked under her bed and
she looked under the table.
But Moo was not there.

Tamla was sad.
She didn't want to drink
her milk without Moo.
"I must do the washing," said Mum.

Mum got the washing ready to put
into the washing machine.
She opened the door of the machine.
"Oh!" said Mum.
"Oh!" said Tamla.

Inside the washing machine they saw
a ball of wool,
a nice warm scarf and
a pair of socks . . . and Moo.

There were four fluffy little kittens
inside the washing machine too.
Moo was licking them and
they were making little noises.
"Moo-oo-oo," they said, which
was more like a moo than a mew.

Things to talk about

1. What sort of noises did Tamla's cat make?
Can you find the words in the story?

2. Did you guess where Moo was?
Why do you think Tamla and her Mum said "Oh!"?

3. Why was the cat called Moo?

Do you have any pets? What are their names?

Why were they given these names?

If you don't have a pet, choose an animal for a pet.
What name would you give it? Why?

Looking at pictures and words

1. Can you remember what was said about Moo in the story?

The lines below have got the words at the end mixed up. Can you sort them out and write down the lines correctly, without looking back at the story?

tickle-your-bed

snuffle-your-nose

play-with-your-ear

lie-on-your-wool

2. What had Mum lost? What did she say?

What had Dad lost? What did he say?

What had Tamla lost? What did she say?

3. Who said "I must do the washing."

Who said "Moo, Moo, where are you?"

Who said "Where's my scarf?"

4. Copy out the words in the story that begin with m

Can you read aloud the words you have written?

Things to do

1. Draw all the things that were in the washing machine.

2. Can you say which word is not a noise?

mew   purr   tickle   hiss

3. Find these words in this ball of wool. Copy them out.

milk   cat   Moo   nest

These activities and skills:	will help your children to:
Looking and remembering	hold a story in their heads, retell it in their own words.
Listening, being able to tell the difference between sounds	remember sounds in words and link spoken words with the words they see in print.
Naming things and using different words to explain or retell events	recognise different words in print, build their vocabulary and guess at the meaning of words.
Matching, seeing patterns, similarities and differences	recognise letters, see patterns within words, use the patterns to read 'new' words and split long words into syllables.
Knowing the grammatical patterns of spoken language	guess the word-order in reading.
Anticipating what is likely to happen next in a story	guess what the next sentence or event is likely to be about.
Colouring, getting control of pencils and pens, copying and spelling	produce their own writing, which will help them to understand the way English is written.
Understanding new experiences by linking them to what they already know	read with understanding and think about what they have read.
Understanding their own feelings and those of others	enjoy and respond to stories and identify with the characters.

First published 1989 by Pan Books Ltd,
Cavaye Place, London SW10 9PG

9 8 7 6 5 4 3 2 1

Editorial consultant: Donna Bailey

© Pan Books Ltd and Macmillan Publishers Ltd 1989. Text © Helen Arnold 1989

British Library Cataloguing in Publication Data
Arnold, Helen
Tamla's cat.
1. English language. Readers – For children
I. Title   II. Series
428.6
ISBN 0–330–30567–0

Printed in Hong Kong